play BASS with...

LINKIN PARK
LIMP BIZKIT
SYSTEM OF A DOWN
P.O.D.
PAPA ROACH
MARILYN MANSON

Wise Publications London / New York / Paris / Sydney / Copenhagen / Berlin / Madrid / Tokyo

Exclusive Distributors:
Music Sales Limited
8/9 Frith Street, London W1D 3JB, England.
Music Sales Pty Limited
120 Rothschild Avenue, Rosebery, NSW 2018, Australia.

Order No. AM974974
ISBN 0-7119-9558-3
This book © Copyright 2002 by Wise Publications.

Compiled by Nick Crispin.
Music arranged by Arthur Dick and Paul Townsend.
Music processed by Paul Ewers Music Design.
Cover photograph courtesy of Redferns.

Printed in the United Kingdom by
Caligraving Limited, Thetford, Norfolk.

CD recorded, mixed and mastered by Jonas Persson
Guitars by Arthur Dick
Bass Guitar by Paul Townsend
Drums by Brett Morgan

www.musicsales.com

play BASS with...

BASS GUITAR
TABLATURE EXPLAINED

Bass Tablature *is a four-line staff that graphically represents the bass fingerboard. By placing a number on the appropriate line,*
the string and fret of any note can be indicated. The number 0 represents an open string. For example:

3rd string, 3rd fret   4th string, open

SLIDE (not restruck): Strike the first note and then slide the same fret-hand finger up or down to the second note.

SLIDE (with restrike): Same as previous slide, except the second note is struck.

SLIDE: Slide up to the note indicated from a few notes below.

SLIDE: Strike the note indicated and slide up an indefinite number of frets.

HAMMER-ON: Strike the first (lower) note with one finger, then sound the higher note (on the same string) with another finger by fretting it without picking.

PULL-OFF: Place both fingers on the notes to be sounded. Strike the first note and without picking, pull the finger off to sound the second lower note.

PALM-MUTE: The note is partially muted by the pick hand lightly touching the string(s) just before the bridge.

MUFFLED-STRINGS: A percussive sound is produced by laying the left hand across the string(s) without depressing it to the fretboard.

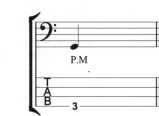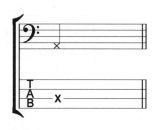

BEND (half step): Strike the note and bend up a semi-tone (half step).

BEND & RELEASE: Strike the note and bend up as indicated, then release back to the original note.

PRE-BEND: Bend the note as indicated then strike it.

PRE-BEND & RELEASE: Bend the note as indicated. Strike it and release the note back to the original pitch.

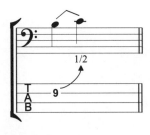

TRILLS: Very rapidly alternate between the notes indicated by continuously hammering on and pulling off.

VIBRATO: The string is vibrated by rapidly bending and releasing the note with the fretting hand.

NATURAL HARMONIC: Strike the note while the fret-hand lightly touches the string directly over the fret indicated.

TREMOLO PICKING: The note is picked as rapidly and continuously as possible.

NOTE: The speed of any bend is indicated by the music notation and tempo.

ALIVE

Words & Music by P.O.D.

5 string bass/pick
4 string bass part in *italics*

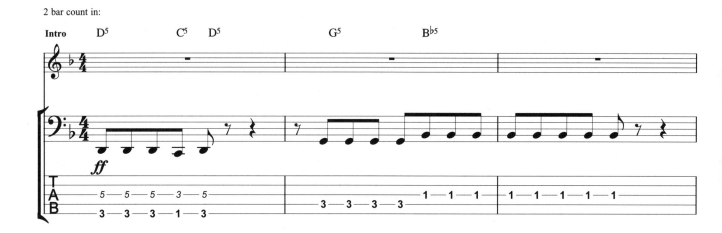

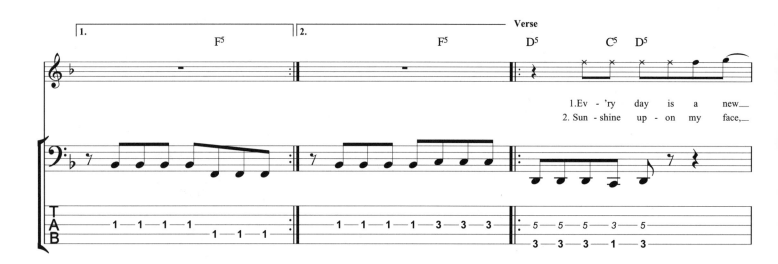

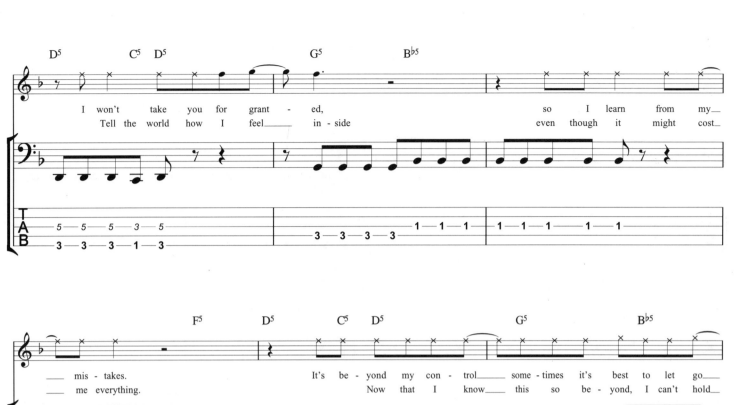

I won't take you for grant - ed,   so I learn from my___
Tell the world how I feel___ in - side   even though it might cost___

___ mis - takes.   It's be - yond my con - trol___ some - times it's best to let go___
___ me everything.   Now that I know___ this so be - yond, I can't hold___

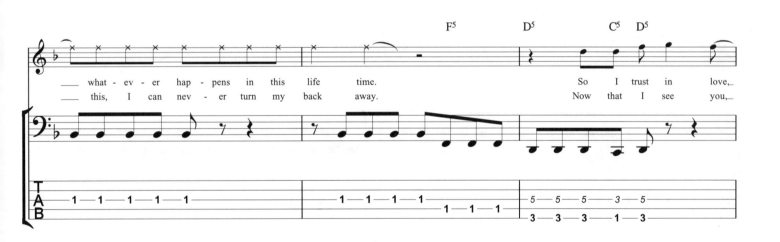

___ what - ev - er hap - pens in this life time.   So I trust in love,___
___ this, I can nev - er turn my back away.   Now that I see you,___

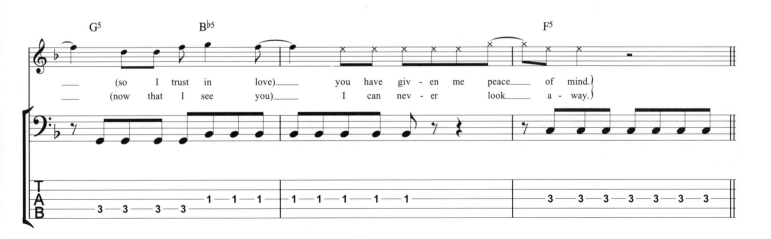

___ (so I trust in love)___ you have giv - en me peace___ of mind.)
___ (now that I see you)___ I can nev - er look___ a - way.)

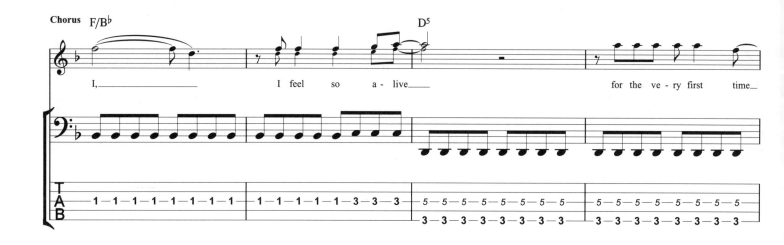

Chorus

I,_____ I feel so a-live_____ for the ve-ry first time_____

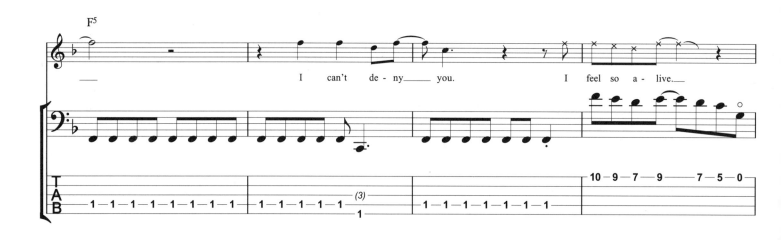

_____ I can't de-ny_____ you. I feel so a-live._____

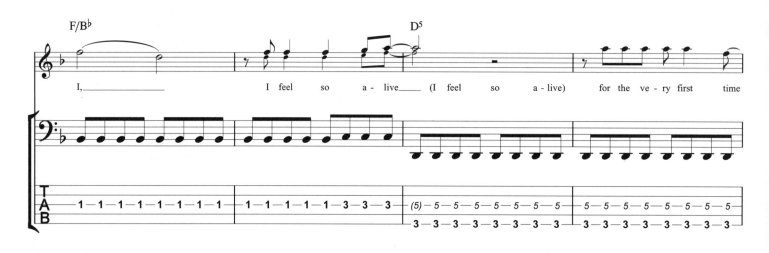

I,_____ I feel so a-live_____ (I feel so a-live) for the ve-ry first time

1.

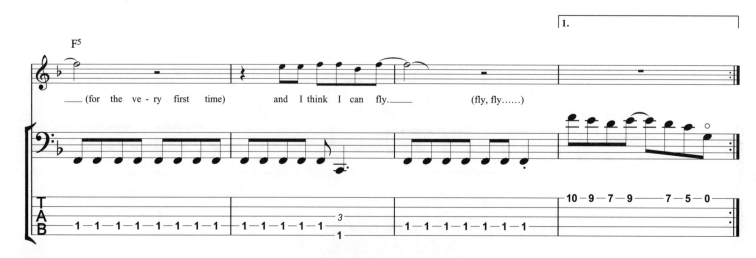

_____ (for the ve-ry first time) and I think I can fly._____ (fly, fly......)

Bridge

w/ad lib. vocal fx

And now that I know___

___ you___ I could nev - er turn my back a - way.__ And now that I see___

___ you, I could nev - er look___ a - way.__ And now that I know___

9

BETWEEN ANGELS AND INSECTS

Words & Music by Papa Roach

5 string bass/pick
4 string bass part in *italics*

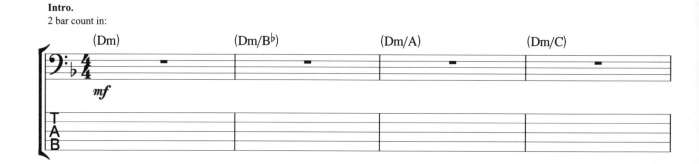

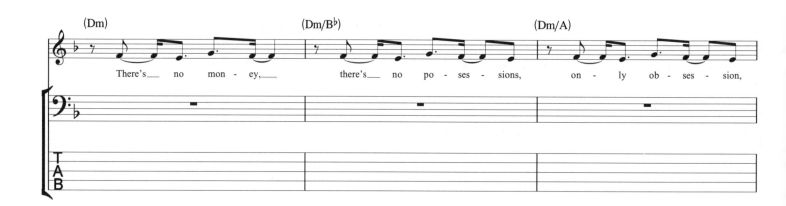

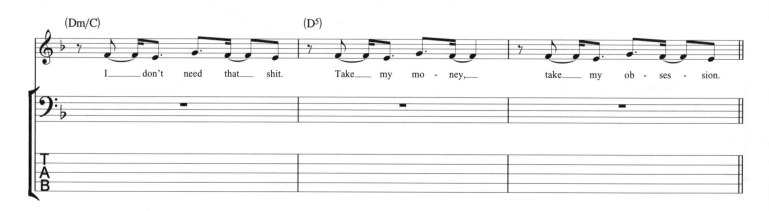

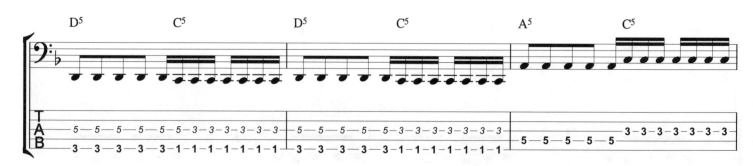

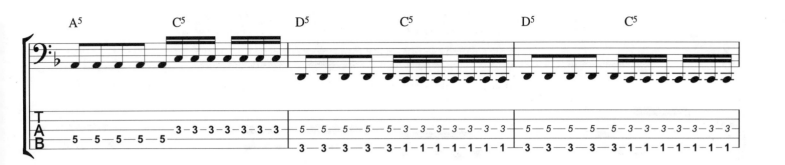

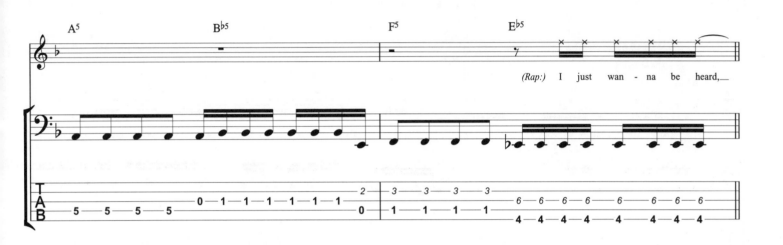

(Rap:) I just wan - na be heard,

Verse

loud and clear are my words, com - ing from with - in, man, tell me what you heard.

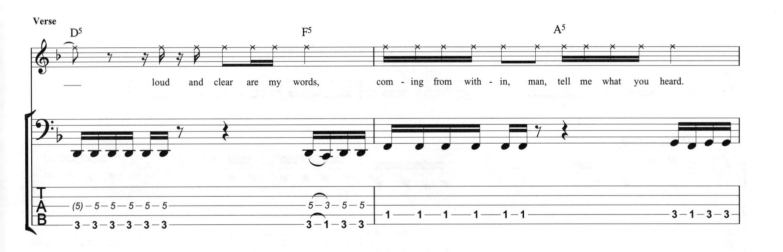

It's a - bout a re - vo - lu - tion, in your heart and in your mind you can find a con - clu - sion.

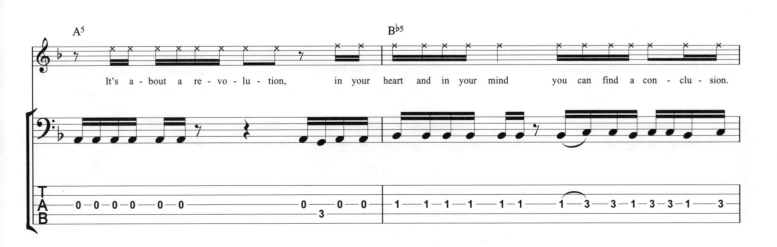

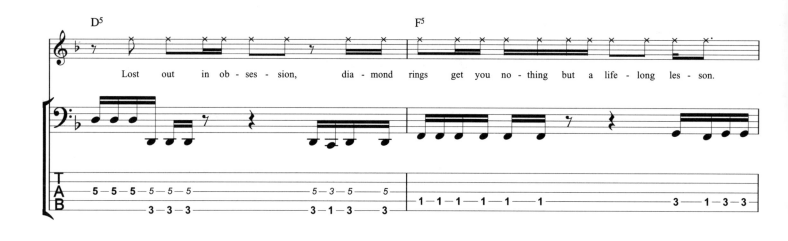

Lost out in ob-ses-sion, dia-mond rings get you no-thing but a life-long les-son.

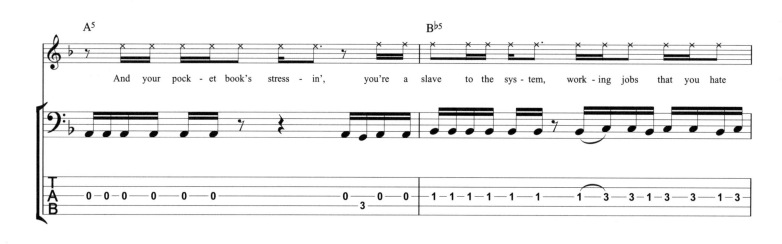

And your pock-et book's stress-in', you're a slave to the sys-tem, work-ing jobs that you hate

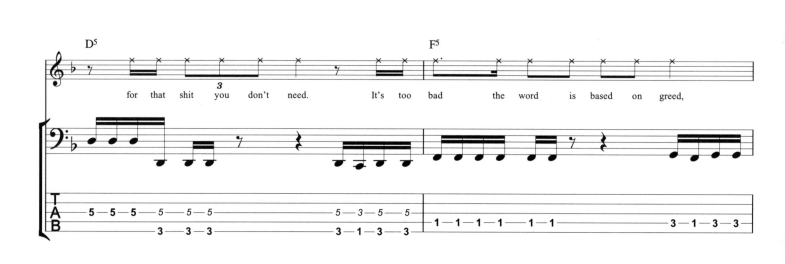

for that shit you don't need. It's too bad the word is based on greed,

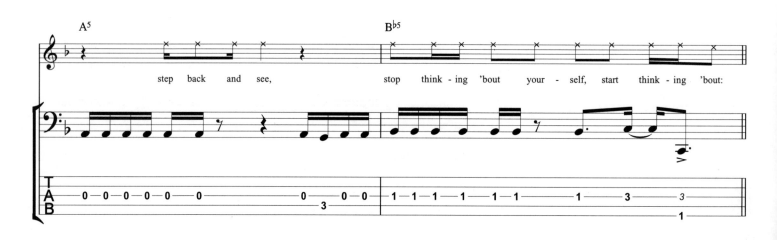

step back and see, stop think-ing 'bout your-self, start think-ing 'bout:

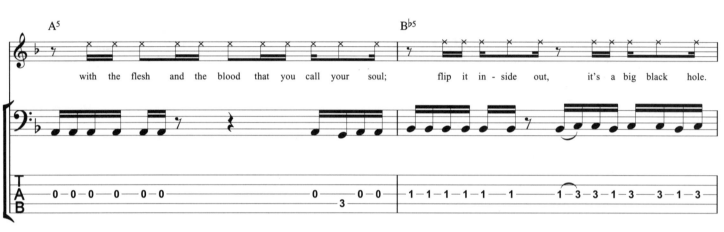

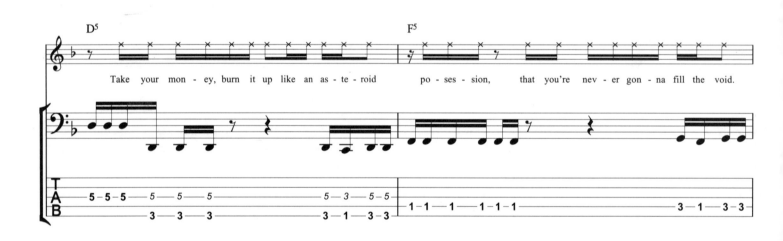

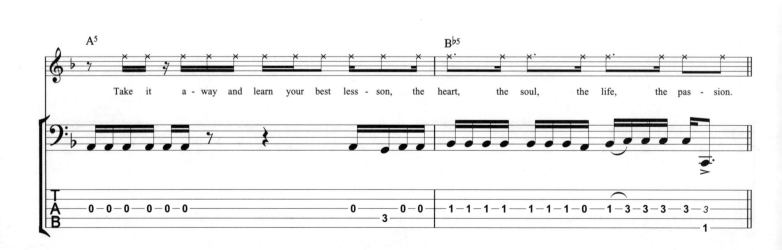

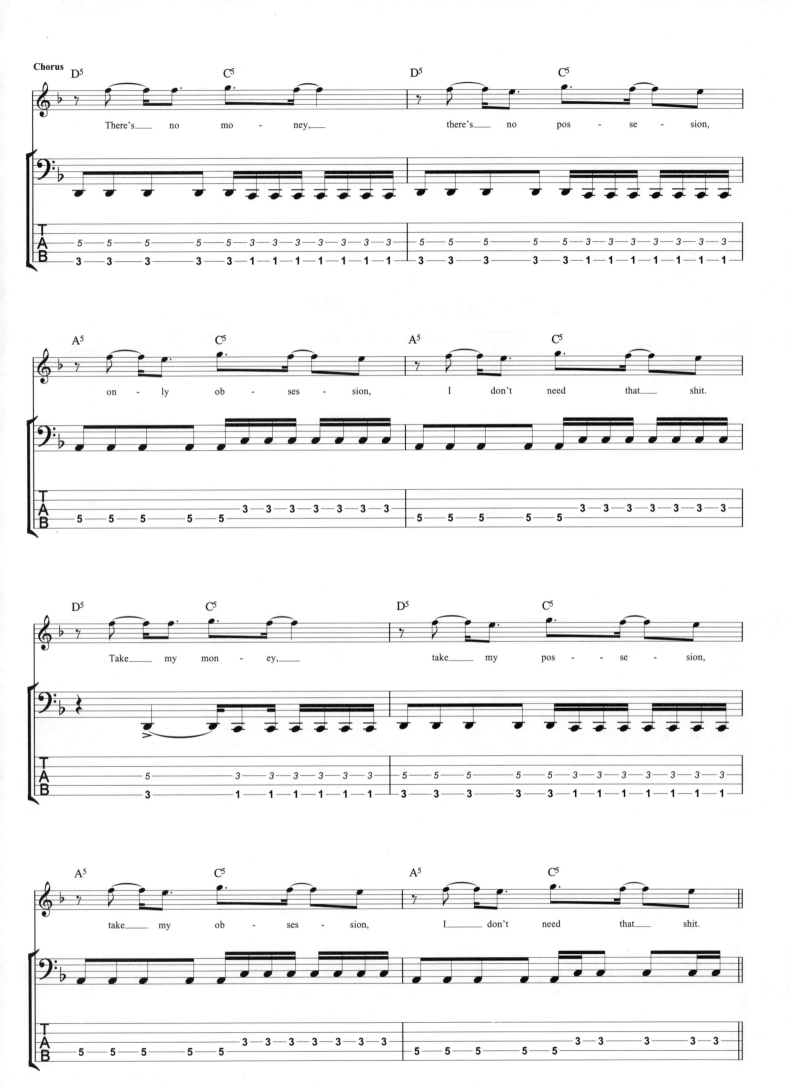

and the things you own,_____ own_____ you. No!

Chorus

Take_____ my mo - ney,_____ take_____ my po - ses - sion,

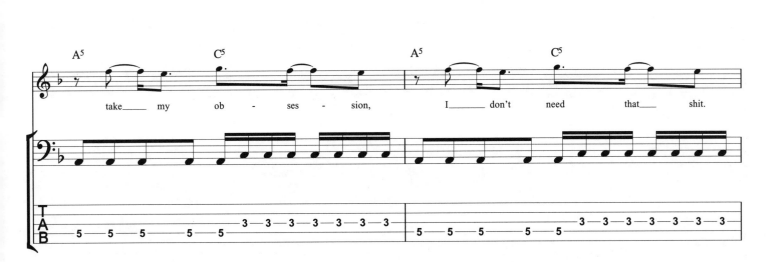

take_____ my ob - ses - sion, I_____ don't need that_____ shit.

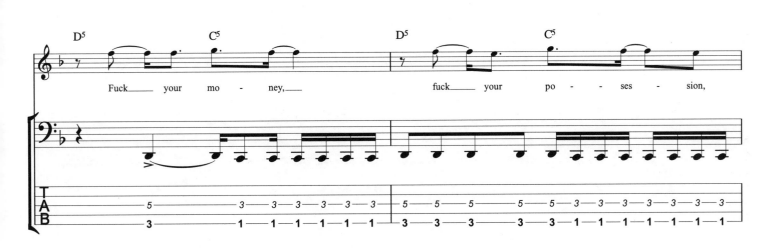

Fuck_____ your mo - ney,_____ fuck_____ your po - - ses - sion,

CHOP SUEY!

Words by Serj Tankian & Daron Malakian
Music by Daron Malakian

5 string bass/pick
4 string bass part in *italics*

2 bar count in:

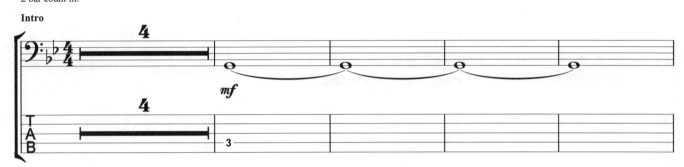

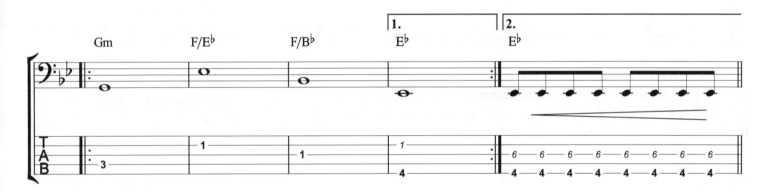

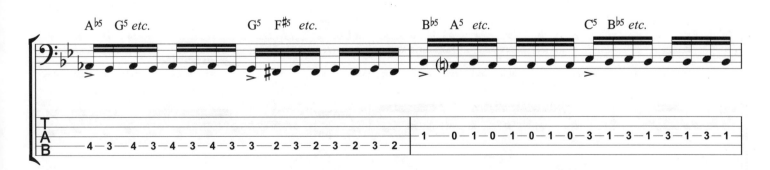

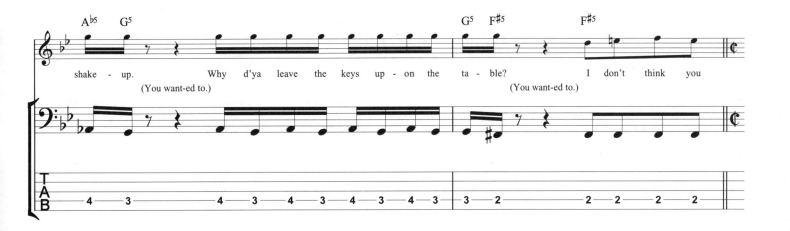

shake - up.   Why d'ya leave the keys up - on the ta - ble?   I don't think you
(You want-ed to.)   (You want-ed to.)

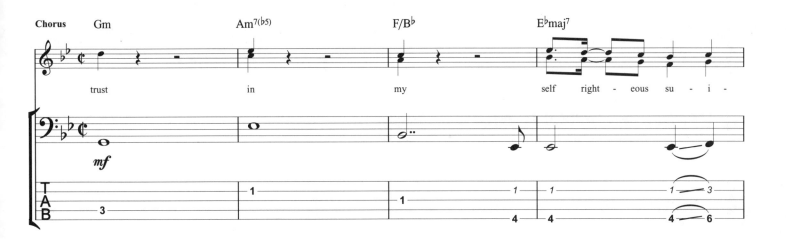

trust   in   my   self right - eous su - i -

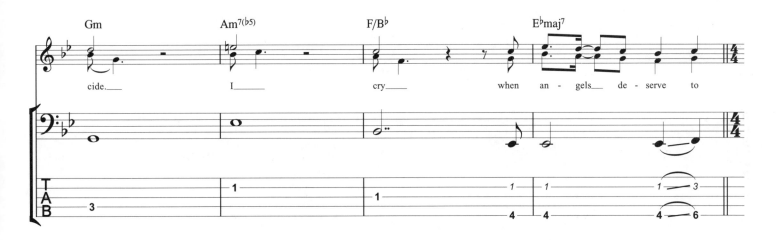

cide.___   I___   cry___   when an - gels___ de - serve to

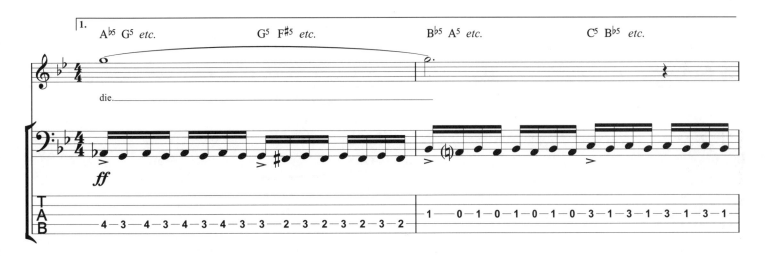

die.___

23

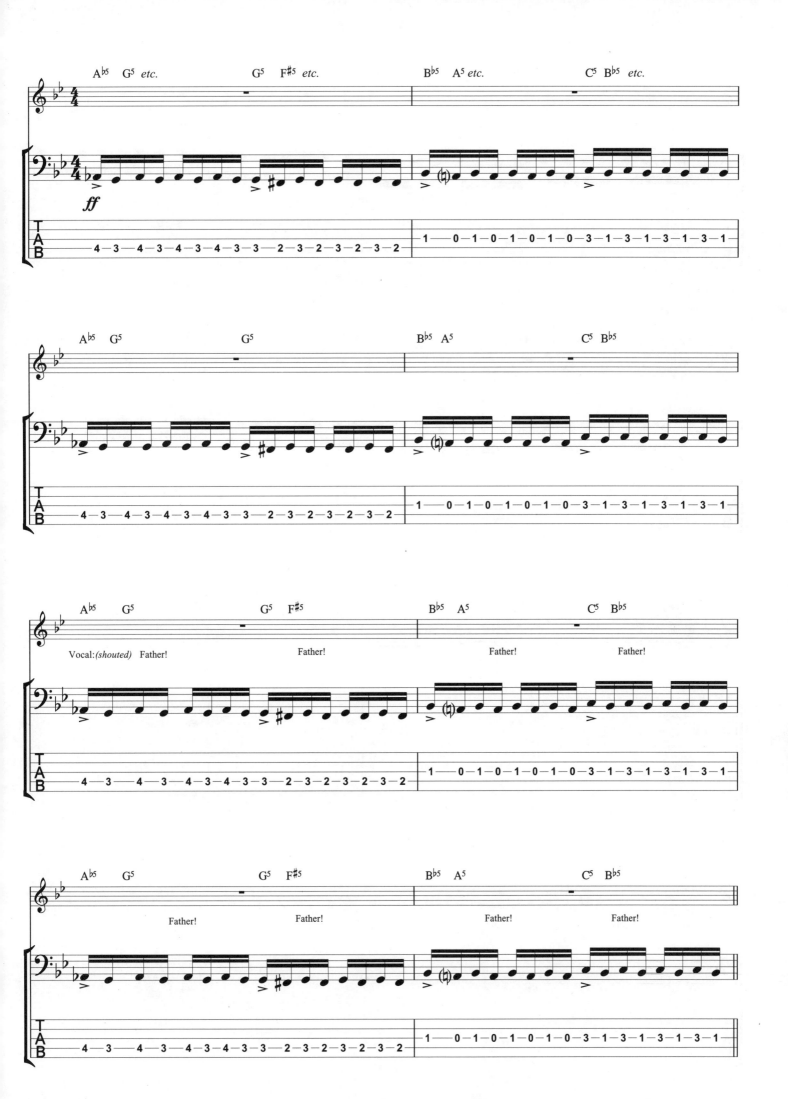

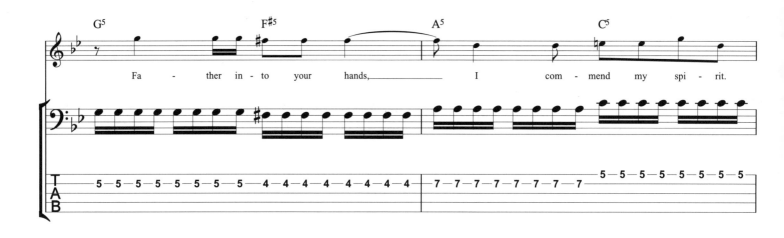

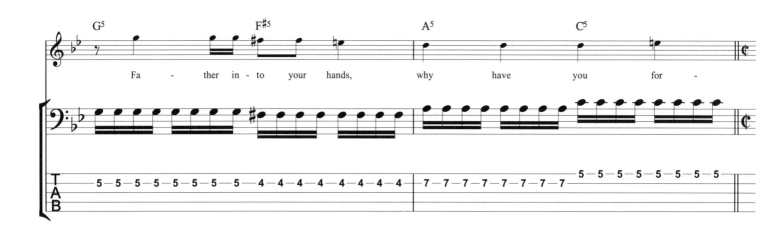

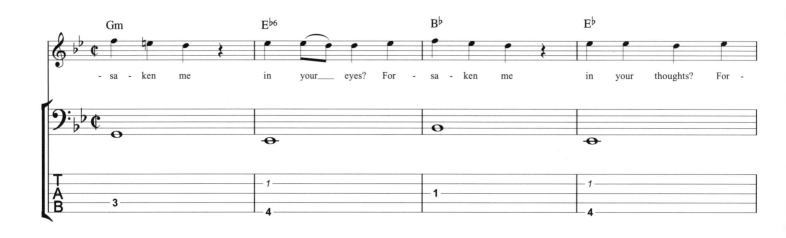

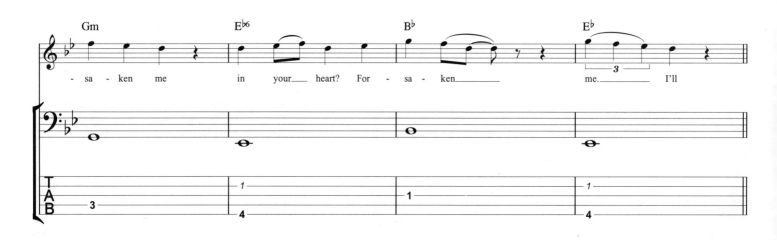

CRAWLING

Words & Music by Chester Bennington, Rob Bourdon, Brad Delson, Joseph Hahn & Mike Shinoda

5 string bass
4 string bass part in *italics*

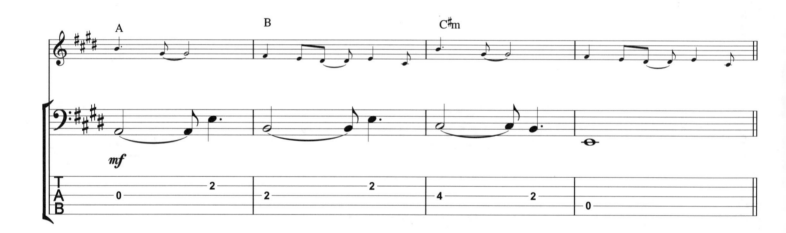

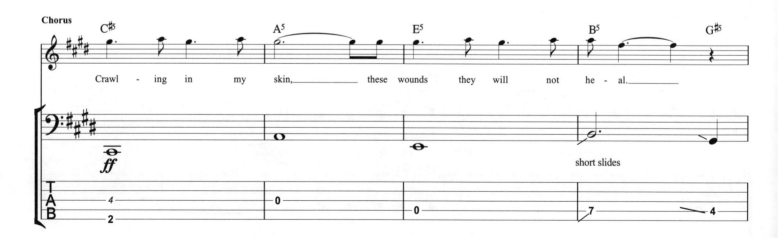

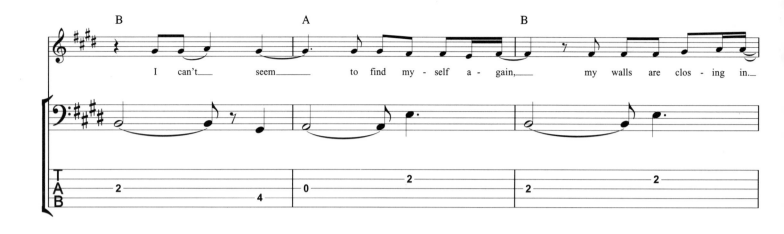

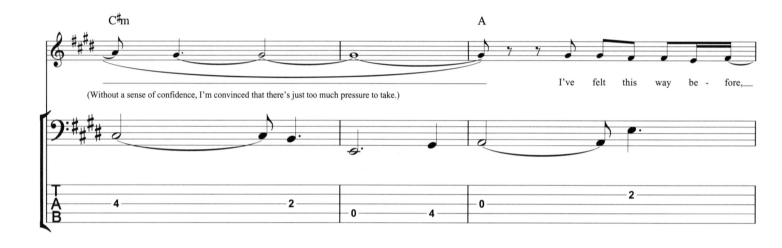

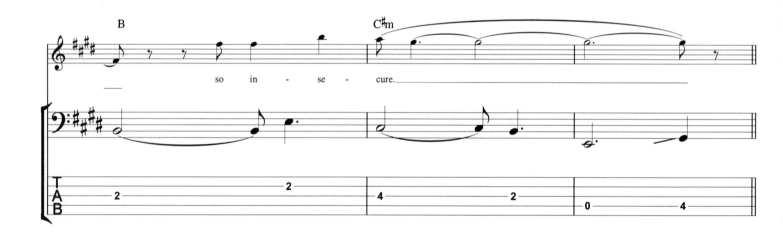

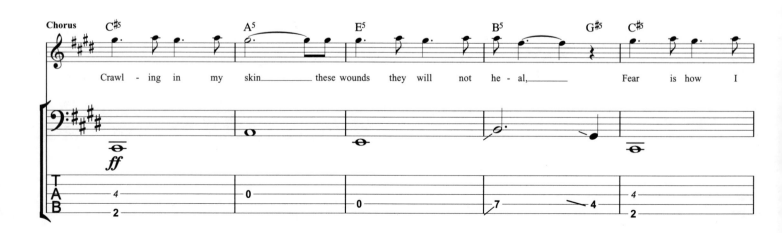

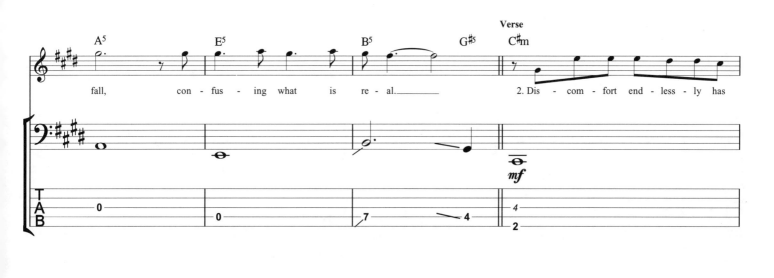

fall, con - fus - ing what is re - al._____ 2. Dis - com - fort end - less - ly has

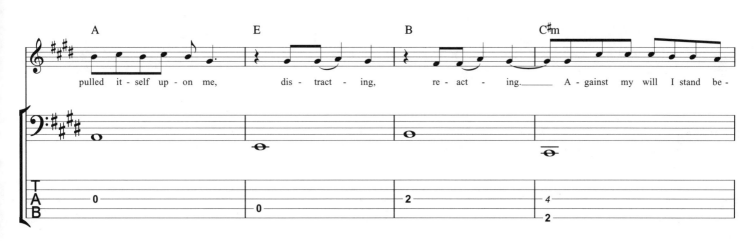

pulled it - self up - on me, dis - tract - ing, re - act - ing._____ A - gainst my will I stand be -

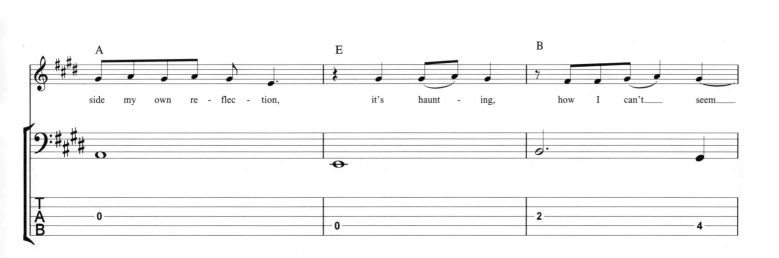

side my own re - flec - tion, it's haunt - ing, how I can't_____ seem_____

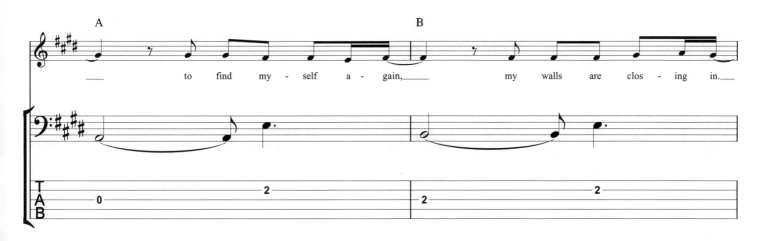

_____ to find my - self a - gain,_____ my walls are clos - ing in._____

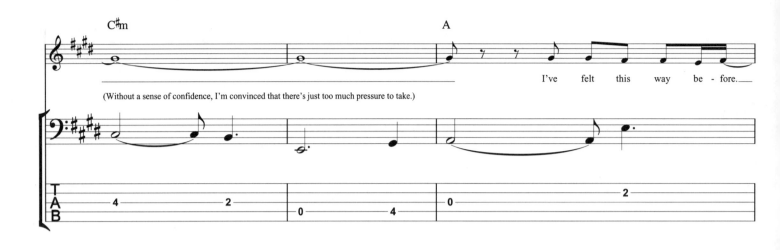

(Without a sense of confidence, I'm convinced that there's just too much pressure to take.)

I've felt this way be-fore.

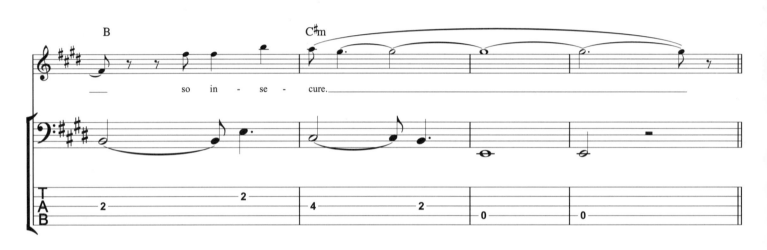

so in-se-cure.

Chorus

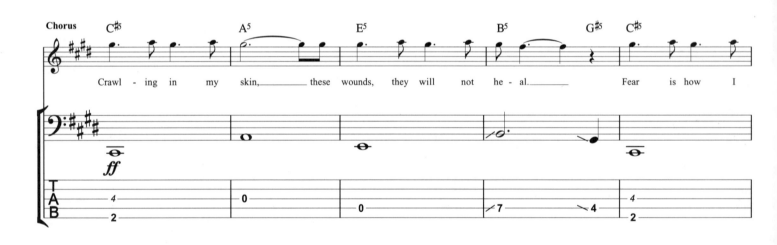

Crawl-ing in my skin, these wounds, they will not he-al. Fear is how I

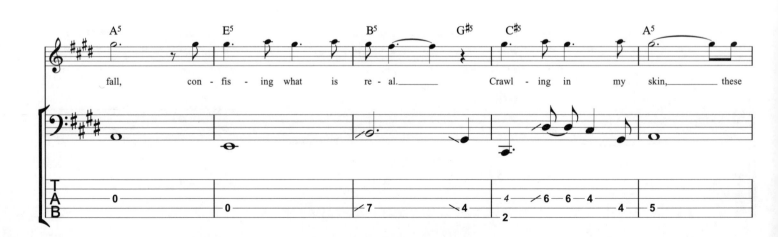

fall, con-fis-ing what is re-al. Crawl-ing in my skin, these

THE FIGHT SONG

Words & Music by Brian Warner & John Lowery

4 or 5 string bass

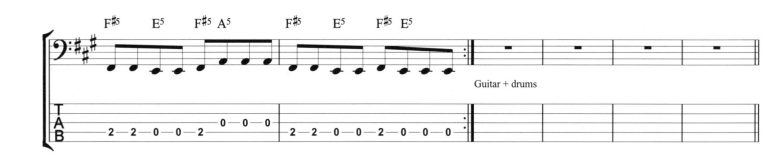

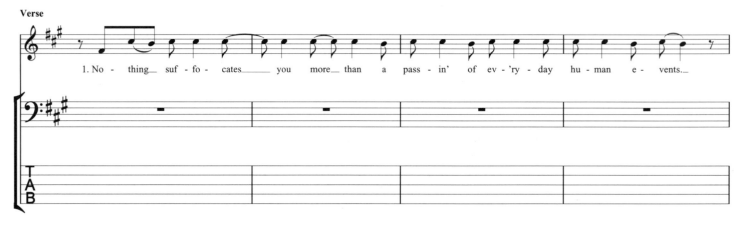

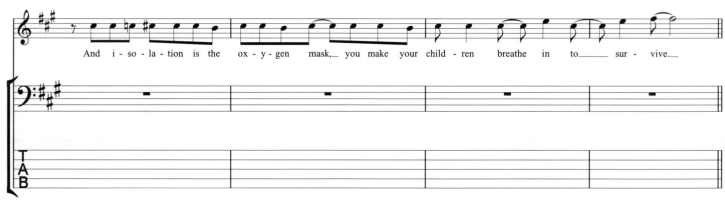

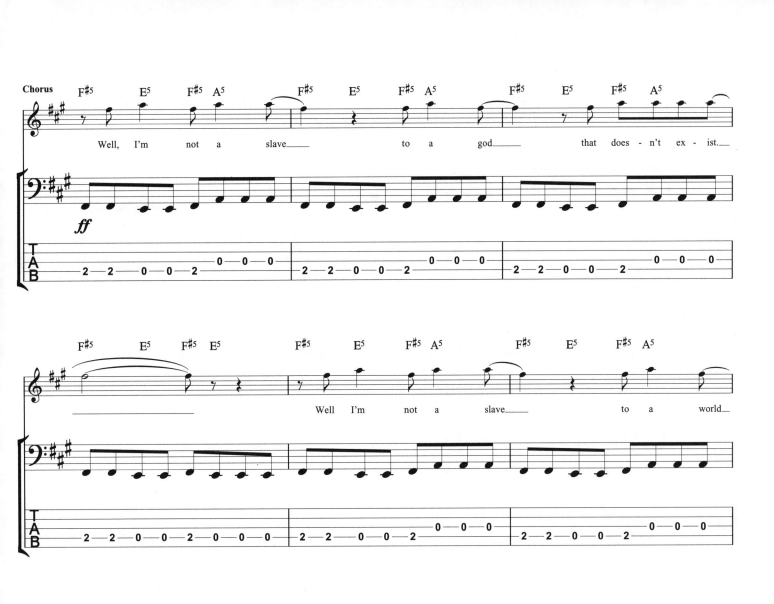

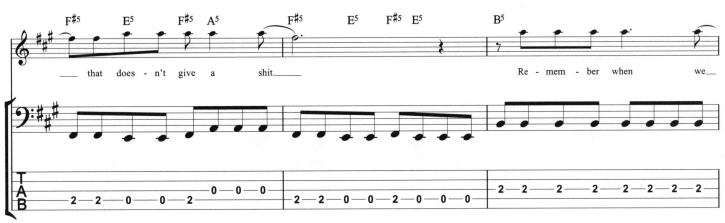

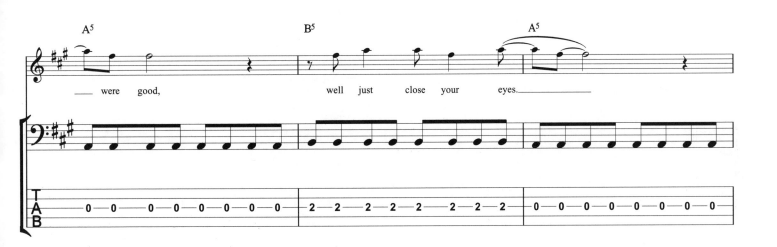

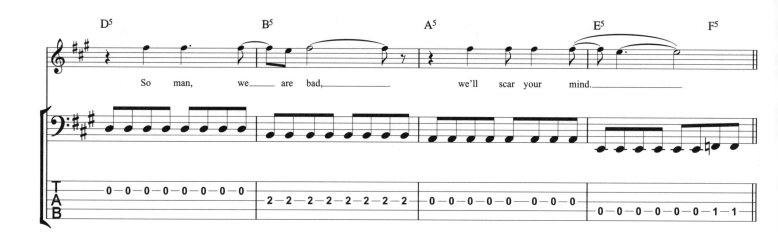

So man, we___ are bad,_____ we'll scar your mind._____

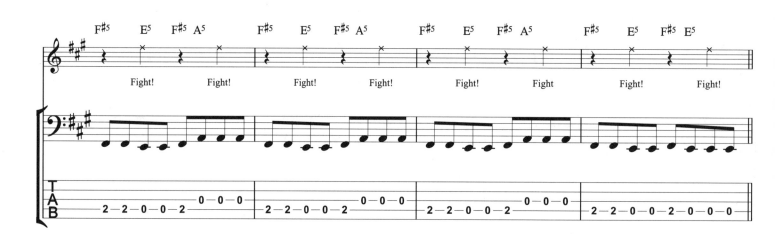

Fight!   Fight!   Fight!   Fight!   Fight!   Fight   Fight!   Fight!

Verse

2. You'll nev - er grow up to be_____ a big rock star, ce - le - bra - ted vic - tim of_____ your fame._____

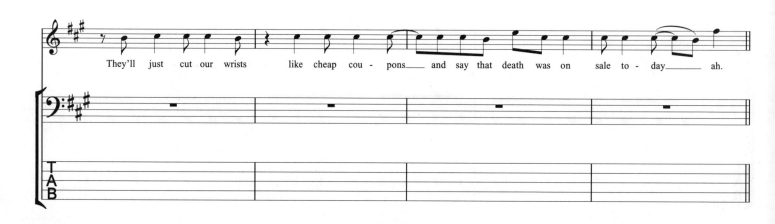

They'll just cut our wrists like cheap cou - pons____ and say that death was on sale to - day_____ ah.

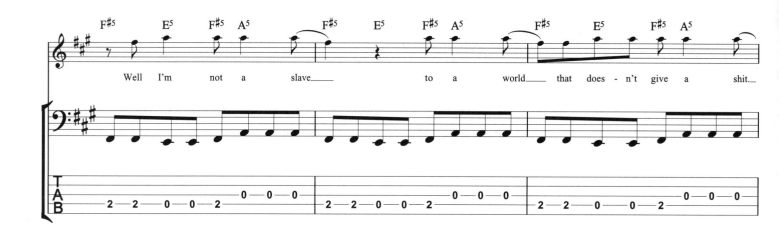

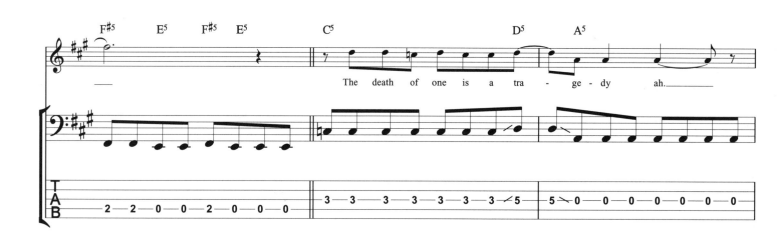

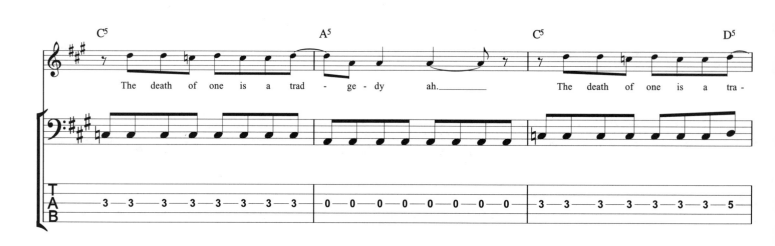

MY GENERATION

Words by Fred Durst
Music by Wes Borland, Sam Rivers & John Otto

5 string bass

If on - ly we could fly. Limp Biz - kit style;

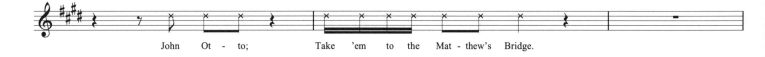

John Ot - to; Take 'em to the Mat - thew's Bridge.

Can you feel it? A - g - g ge - ne - ra - tion.

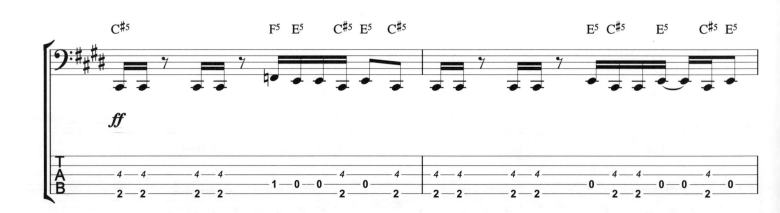

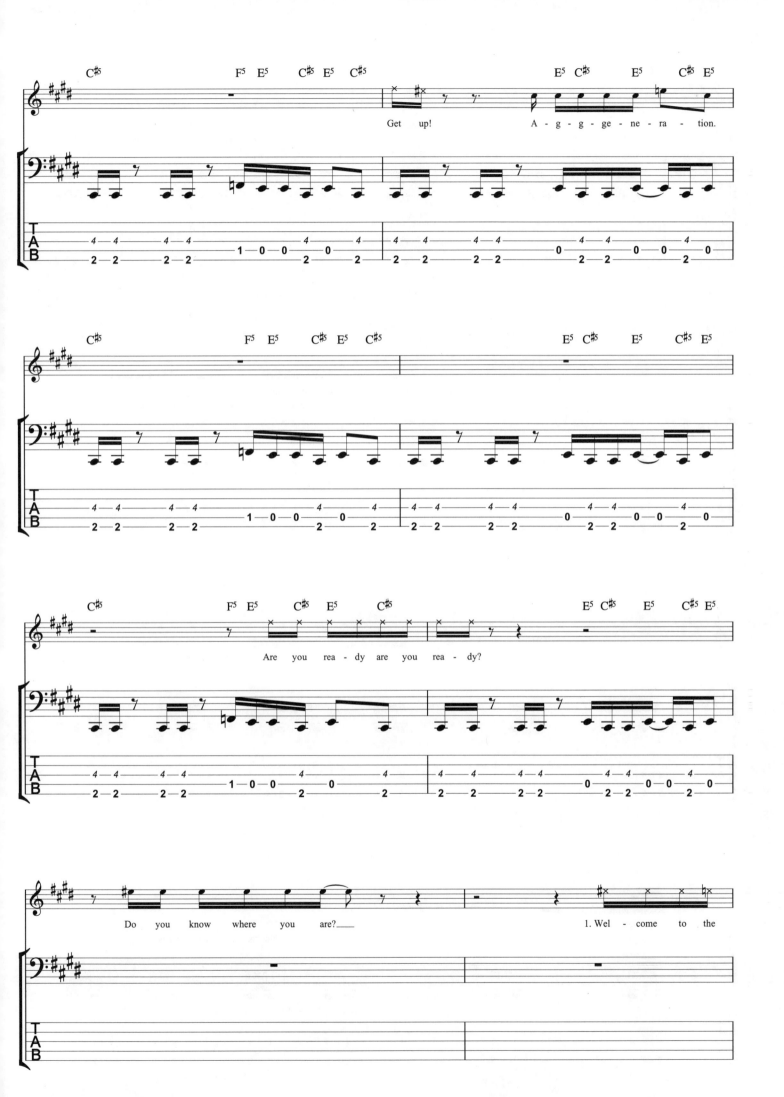

41

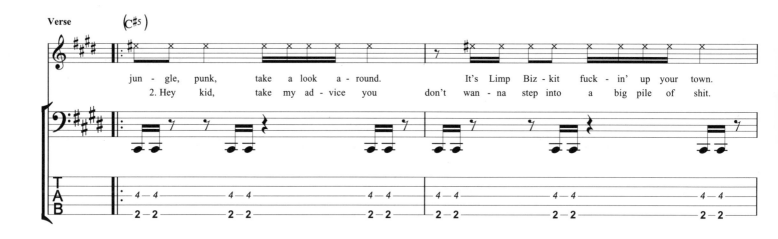

Verse (C#5)

jun - gle, punk, take a look a - round. It's Limp Biz - kit fuck - in' up your town.
2. Hey kid, take my ad - vice you don't wan - na step into a big pile of shit.

We've down - load - ed the Shock - wave, put all the la - dies in the cave to get your groove on.
Caap - tain's drunk,__ your world Ti - ta - nic, float - ing on the funk, so get your groove on.

And may - be I'm the one who flew ov - er the cuck - oo's nest. Well guess who's next?
And may - be I am just a little fucked up, life's just a little fucked up.

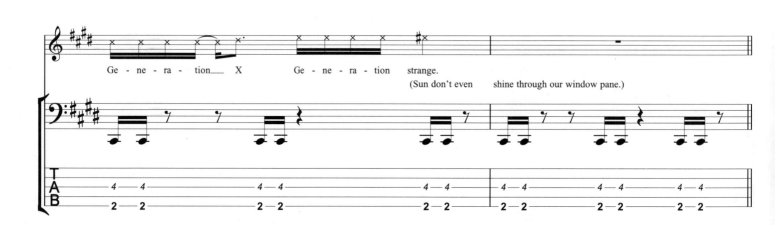

Ge - ne - ra - tion__ X Ge - ne - ra - tion strange.
(Sun don't even shine through our window pane.)

42

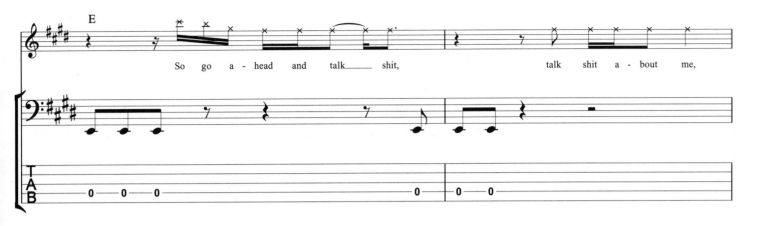

So go a-head and talk____ shit, talk shit a-bout me,

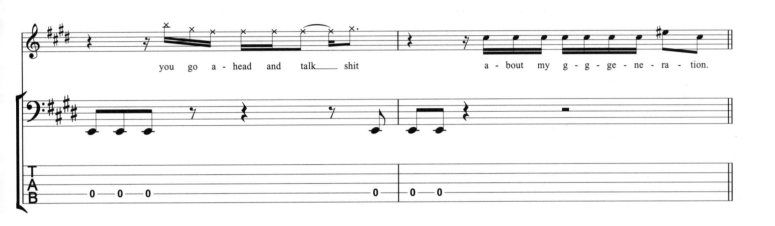

you go a-head and talk____ shit a-bout my g-g-ge-ra-tion.

Chorus

'Cause we don't, don't give a fuck and we won't ev-er give a fuck un-

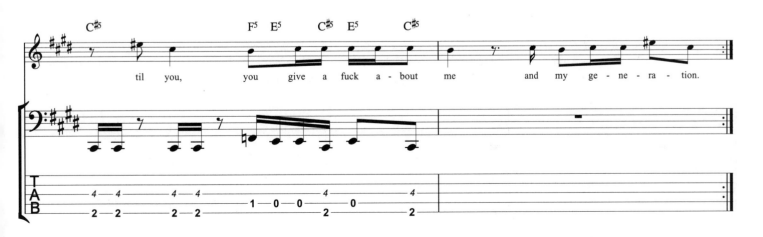

til you, you give a fuck a-bout me and my ge-ne-ra-tion.

'Cause we don't, don't give a fuck and we won't ev - er give a fuck un -

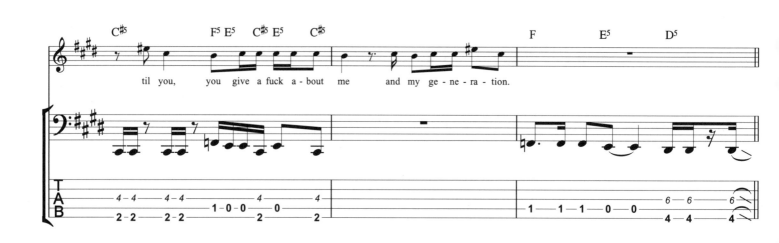

til you, you give a fuck a - bout me and my ge - ne - ra - tion.

Slightly slower

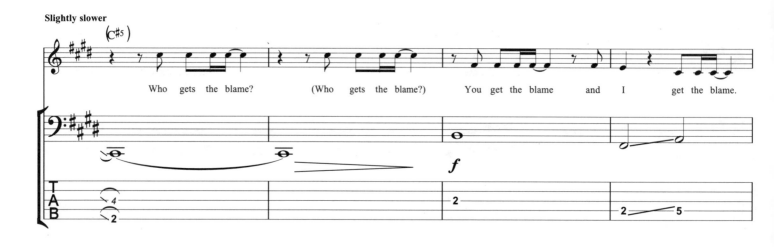

Who gets the blame? (Who gets the blame?) You get the blame and I get the blame.

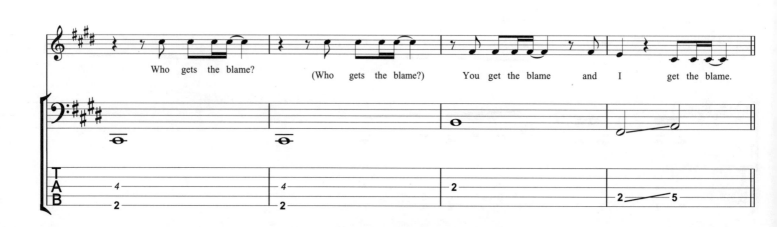

Who gets the blame? (Who gets the blame?) You get the blame and I get the blame.

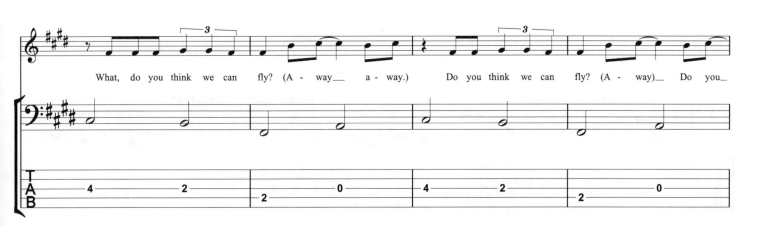

What, do you think we can fly? (A - way___ a - way.) Do you think we can fly? (A - way)___ Do you___

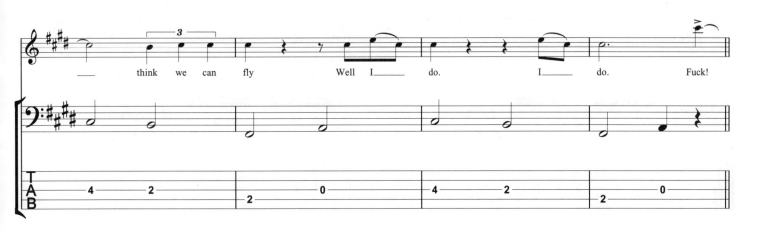

___ think we can fly Well I___ do. I___ do. Fuck!

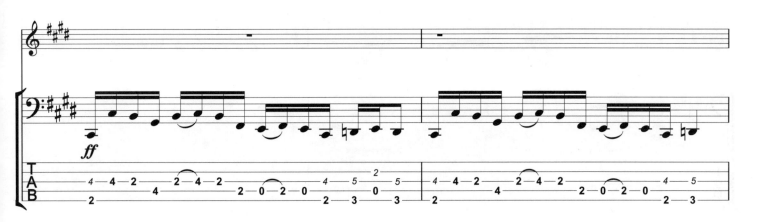

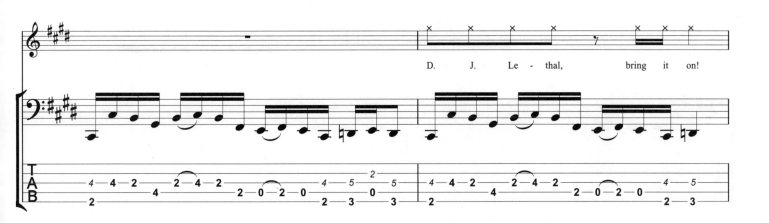

D. J. Le - thal, bring it on!

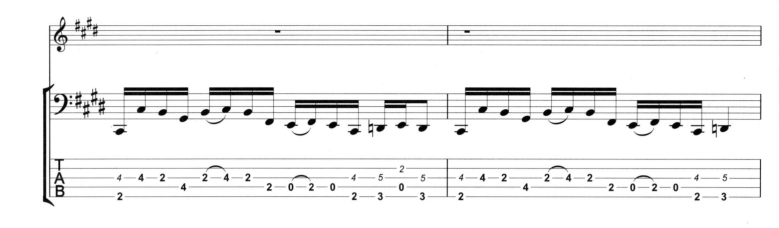

Oh,_____ yeah, c'm - on.

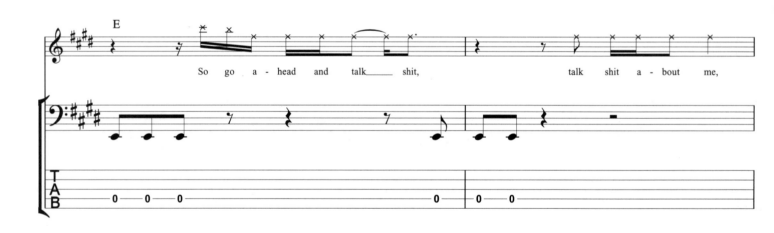

So go a - head and talk____ shit, talk shit a - bout me,

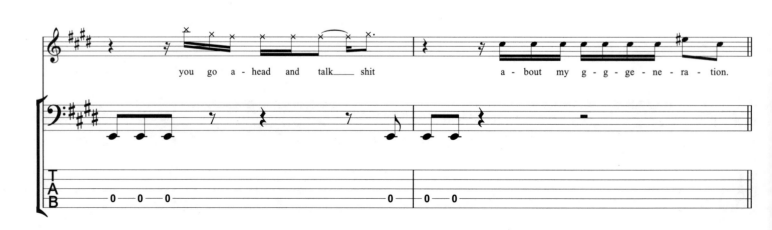

you go a - head and talk____ shit a - bout my g - g - ge - ne - ra - tion.

46

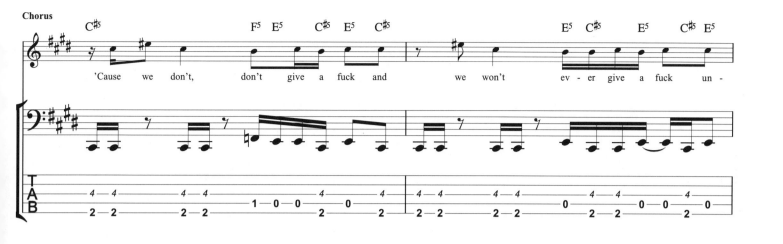

Chorus

'Cause we don't, don't give a fuck and we won't ev-er give a fuck un-

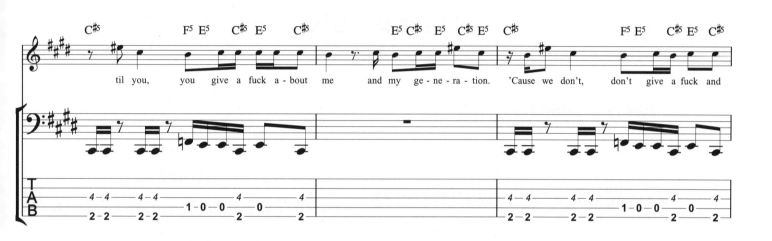

til you, you give a fuck a-bout me and my ge-ne-ra-tion. 'Cause we don't, don't give a fuck and

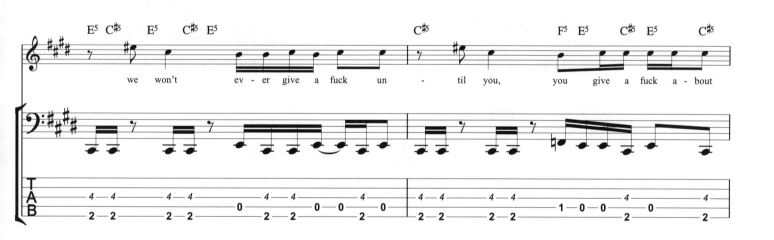

we won't ev-er give a fuck un-til you, you give a fuck a-bout

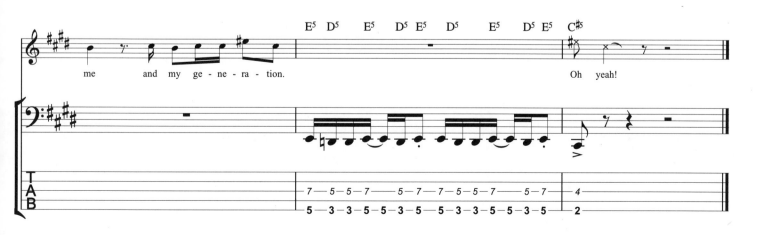

me and my ge-ne-ra-tion. Oh yeah!

47

CD Track Listing

1. TUNING NOTES

**FULL INSTRUMENTAL PERFORMANCES
(WITH BASS)...**

2. ALIVE

(P.O.D.) Famous Music Publishing Ltd

3. BETWEEN ANGELS AND INSECTS

(Papa Roach) Cherry Lane Music Ltd

4. CHOP SUEY!

(Tankian / Malakian) Sony / ATV Music Publishing (UK) Ltd

5. CRAWLING

(Bennington / Bourdon / Delson / Hahn / Shinoda) Zomba Music Publishers Ltd

6. THE FIGHT SONG

(Warner / Lowery) EMI Music Publishing Limited / Chrysalis Music Ltd

7. MY GENERATION

(Durst / Borland / Rivers / Otto) Zomba Music Publishers Ltd

**BACKING TRACKS ONLY
(WITHOUT BASS)...**

8. ALIVE

9. BETWEEN ANGELS AND INSECTS

10. CHOP SUEY!

11. CRAWLING

12. THE FIGHT SONG

13. MY GENERATION

To remove your CD from the plastic sleeve, lift the small lip on the right to break the perforated flap.
Replace the disc after use for convenient storage.